WALKABOUT

In the Air

© 1993 Franklin Watts

Franklin Watts
96 Leonard Street
London EC2A 4RH

Franklin Watts Australia
14 Mars Road
Lane Cove
NSW 2066

UK ISBN: 0 7496 1080 8

10 9 8 7 6 5 4 3 2 1

A CIP catalogue record for this book
is available from the British Library

Editor: Ambreen Husain
Design: Volume One

Printed in Hong Kong

Photographs: Aviation Picture Library
(A J Brown) 22, 26, 27, (T Joint) 24;
Bruce Coleman Ltd (J Burton) 8 inset,
(P Terry) 9 inset, (K Taylor) 13, 14,
(J Rydell) 16, (E Crichton) 25; Eye Ubiquitous
9, 12 inset, 29; Chris Fairclough Colour
Library 6, 24 inset, 30; Robert Harding
23, 30 inset; Frank Lane Pictue Agency
11, 21; NHPA (S Dalton) cover, 8, 10, 15, 17,
19, 20, (M Danegger) 18, (D Woodfall) 31;
ZEFA 4, 5, 7, 12, 28.

Additional photographs: Stephen Oliver

Fife
COUNCIL
King's Road Primary School
Rosyth - Tel: 313470

WALKABOUT
In the Air

Henry Pluckrose

Franklin Watts
London • New York • Sydney • Toronto

Air is all around us but we cannot see air. Every living thing needs air to stay alive.

Although air is invisible
we can see what happens
when air moves.
What is making this tree
bend and sway?

You can feel air moving
on a windy day.
Wind blows leaves around...

and makes clouds move
across the sky.
Have you ever
flown a kite
on a windy day?

Many flowers and plants
spread their seeds
by letting them float
through the air.
Some are carried long distances
by the wind.
The seeds of the sycamore tree
spin through the air
to the ground...

and the seeds of the dandelion
float through the air
on a tiny parachute of fine down.
A parachute is shaped
to use air as a brake
to slow it down.

Not everything which moves
through the air relies on
the wind and breeze.
A moth uses its wings
to fly from plant to plant.

A butterfly looks rather like
a moth.
Moths are usually active
at night
and butterflies fly around
during the day.

Moths and butterflies
are insects.
The ladybird is also an insect.
When it is not flying
its wings are protected by
spotted wing covers.

Beetles have wing covers too.
When they fly
the wing covers are opened
and spread wide.

Many insects live on
the pollen and nectar
which they collect
from flowers.
Wings help them to move easily
from flower to flower.

Wasps are also flying insects.
They have black and yellow colouring -
just like bees.
The pattern is a warning -
"Don't eat me. I sting!"

There are many flying creatures
larger than insects.
Bats fly mostly in the evening -
just before it is really dark.
The wings of a bat are
hard thin sheets of skin.

The wing of a bird
is covered with feathers.
Each feather is very light.
Birds push themselves
through the air
with their wings.

By rapidly beating
her feathered wings
the swan is able to
lift herself from the water -
and fly.

A hummingbird beats its wings
so quickly that it can stay
still in the air
as it feeds.

The wings of an owl
have special feathers.
These feathers help the owl
to fly silently.

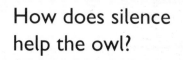

How does silence
help the owl?

Human beings cannot fly.
But they have invented things
to help them move
through the air.
A hot air balloon floats
high above the ground.
It is blown along by the wind.

G-BBCK

The pilot can make it go up
and down
by heating the air
inside the balloon.
But he cannot steer it
just where he pleases.
That depends on the wind!

A glider has no power of its own.
High above the ground,
it glides on moving currents
of air.
Birds often use air currents
to glide.

The pilot of this glider also needs air currents to keep him airborne. Why is this called a hang-glider?

Aircraft have bodies and wings
which are shaped
to help the air lift them up.
This aircraft is powered
by a propellor...

and this giant airliner
is powered by jet engines.

Some aircraft are driven
through the air
by moving rotors.
A helicopter can use its rotors
to hover in one place.
It does not need much space
to take off...

or to land.

Smoke from factories and fires
and exhaust fumes from cars
make the air dirty -
they pollute the air.
If the air becomes too polluted
it is difficult to breathe.

To stay fit and healthy
we need to breath clean air.
Air is important
to every living thing.
We need to look after it.

About this book

Young children acquire much information in an incidental, almost random fashion. Indeed, they learn much just by being alive! The books in this series complement the way in which young children learn. Through photographs and a simple text the readers are encouraged to comment on the world in which they live.

To the young child, life is new and almost everything in the world is of interest. But interest alone is not enough. If a child is to grow intellectually this interest has to be harnessed and extended. This book adopts a well tried and successful method of achieving this end. By focusing upon a particular topic, it invites the reader firstly to look and then to question. The words and photographs provide a starting point for discussion. Discussion also involves listening. The adult who listens to the young reader's observations will quickly realise that children have a very real concern for the environmental issues that confront us all.

Children enjoy having information books read to them just as much as stories and poetry. The younger child may ignore the written words...pictures play an important part in learning, particularly if they encourage talk and visual discrimination.

Henry Pluckrose

King's Road Primary School
Rosyth - Tel: 313470